This MAGIC OF ME journal

belongs to:

Jaden Pelletan

ISBN: 978-1-7325963-1-3

First printing edition 2018.

Design by Elena Reznikova.
Based on a cover design by Mark G.

This journal is meant to be used along with the book, *The Magic of Me: A Kids' Spiritual Guide to Health and Happiness,* available as paperback (ISBN: 978-1-7325963-0-6) and e-book (ISBN: 978-1-7325963-2-0).

Boundless Movement

Visit **www.authorbcummings.com**

Introduction

Dear Reader,

This journal is meant to be used along with the book, *The Magic of Me: A Kids' Spiritual Guide to Health and Happiness*. In this book there are 30 brief chapters, each followed by journal pages. If you don't have a physical copy of the book or prefer not to write in it, then this journal is for you.

After you read or listen to a chapter, you can use the pages in this journal to answer the questions and try the suggested activities.

You came to Earth to live an extraordinary life. It's time to begin!

 Sincerely,
Ms. Becky

You Are A Masterpiece

1. Have you ever seen a masterpiece before? If not, what masterpiece would you like to see? _____

   _____

   _____

   _____

   _____

2. If you have seen a masterpiece before how did it make you feel? If you haven't, how do you imagine the masterpiece would make you feel? _____

   _____

   _____

   _____

   _____

   _____

3. Look into the mirror and give yourself a compliment. Say, "I love you!" and thank yourself for being you. If you feel silly, it's okay. Repeat it each day — soon it won't feel so silly anymore!

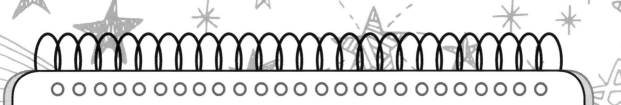

2

You Are More
Than A Body

1. Describe a dream you had recently. How do you think you could see such vivid pictures without using your eyes?

   _____

   _____

   _____

   _____

   _____

   _____

   _____

2. Have you ever noticed you talk to yourself in your head? What are your thoughts right now?_____

   _____

   _____

   _____

   _____

   _____

   _____

Loving Your Body

1. What are five things you can be thankful your body does?

   _____

   _____

   _____

   _____

   _____

2. What choices did you make today that helped your "car" feel and look its best?

   _____

   _____

   _____

   _____

   _____

3. Imagine what it would be like to only have the use of one hand. Wear a sock on your hand for a few hours or even a full day! Talk about your experience with a grownup or friend.

4. Blindfold yourself for a period of time such as 15 minutes. Make sure a grownup is with you for safety. Tell a grownup or friend about your experience.

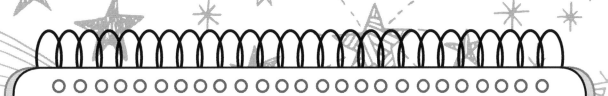

4

You Were Given
Many Gifts

1. What do you like to do or learn about?

   _____

   _____

   _____

   _____

2. How might this be a gift for you?

   _____

   _____

   _____

   _____

3. How might you use this gift to help others?

   _____

   _____

   _____

   _____

4. Write yourself a few sticky notes about what you like
   about yourself. Stick them around your room to remind
   yourself about the gifts you have been given.

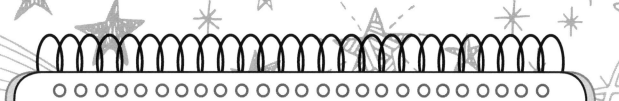

Some Gifts
Are For Others

1. What gift (God given) does a friend have that you have
    wanted?_____

    _____

    _____

    _____

    _____

    _____

2. What compliment can you give him or her?

    _____

    _____

    _____

    _____

    _____

    _____

3. Start a gratitude journal. Take a blank notebook (or use the
    pages at the end of this journal) and at the beginning or end
    of the day write down a few things you are grateful for. It can
    be something specific to that day or something general in
    your life.

    Note: In the back there are some pages to begin your gratitude journal.

6

Your Mind
Is A Garden

1. Explain a time today when you felt a bad feeling like anger or jealousy._____

   _____

   _____

   _____

   _____

2. What thought did you have?

   _____

   _____

   _____

   _____

   _____

3. What thought could you have instead to plant a flower seed? _____

   _____

   _____

   _____

   _____

   _____

7

Your Thoughts Have Power

1. What is one goal you have in the near future?_____

   _____

   _____

   _____

2. What are some positive intentions you could say and write down to help you attract that goal into your life? Start with the words, "I am . . ."_____

   _____

   _____

   _____

3. What can you picture in your mind and feel in your heart to strengthen your powers to attract that goal?_____

   _____

   _____

   _____

4. Create a vision board. Use magazines, the Internet or other resources to collect pictures that represent your future goals. Arrange them on a poster (or the next pages in this journal) so it looks pleasing to you. Write down positive statements on your board that start with, "I am . . ."

My Vision Board

My Vision Board

My Affirmations

I am . . . _____
_____
_____

I am . . . _____
_____
_____

I am . . . _____
_____
_____

I am . . . _____
_____
_____

I am . . . _____
_____
_____

I am . . . _____
_____
_____

8

Your Words
Have Power

1. What is one complaint you say often that is spilling oil into your life?_____

   _____

   _____

2. How can you reword it and change it into fairy dust?

   _____

   _____

   _____

   _____

3. Set up an experiment with two seeds of the same kind from the same packet.

   → Plant them in separate containers and keep everything exactly the same. Make sure they get the same amount of water and sunlight from the same location. The only difference is the words you speak.

   → To one speak loving words telling the plant it is loved, beautiful, and special. To the other say mean words telling it that nobody loves it and it's ugly.

   → Repeat this daily and observe how your plants grow. Share your observations with others.

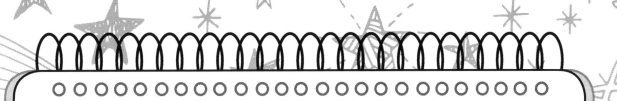

9

Your Actions
Have Power

1. What is one goal you have for the near future you'd like to achieve?_____

   _____

   _____

   _____

2. What actions can you take to help you manifest it, or bring it into your life?

   _____

   _____

   _____

   _____

   _____

3. Why do you think it's important to not give up if you don't reach your goal right away?

   _____

   _____

   _____

   _____

   _____

4. Write down a goal you want to accomplish in the next month. Then break down some action steps you can take to start working toward it. Make them specific which means write down exactly what you will do, how long and how often you will do it.

Goal:

_____

_____

_____

_____

Action Step #1

What I will do:_____

_____

How long:_____

How often:_____

Action Step #2

What I will do:_____

_____

How long:_____

How often:_____

Action Step #3

What I will do:_____

_____

How long:_____

How often:_____

You Can Only Control You

1. What is something bad that happened to you this week?

   _____
   _____
   _____

2. How did you react? Do you think you had lemons or lemonade?

   _____
   _____
   _____
   _____

3. If you had lemons, how could you turn them into lemonade? _____

   _____
   _____
   _____
   _____
   _____
   _____

Connecting To Your Super Powers

1. Do you know anybody that meditates? If so, ask them to share what they do.

   _____
   _____
   _____
   _____

2. What is one of the suggested ways you would like to try?

   _____
   _____
   _____
   _____
   _____
   _____

3. With an adult's guidance, go on the Internet and do a video search for children's meditation. See if there are any that interest you. Try one out!

The Power of Now

1. How is your now?_____

   _____

   _____

   _____

   _____

   _____

   _____

   _____

2. What could you do or think to improve your now?_____

   _____

   _____

   _____

   _____

   _____

   _____

   _____

   _____

   _____

You Can Heal Yourself

1. What is one time you had a bad illness or injury?_____

   _____

   _____

   _____

   _____

   _____

2. Did you heal from it? How do you know you healed?

   _____

   _____

   _____

   _____

   _____

   _____

   _____

   _____

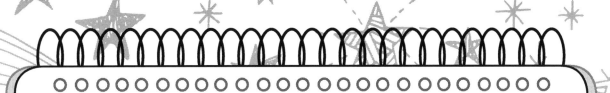

14

Food Is Medicine

1. What are some healthy foods you eat now?_____

    _____

    _____

    _____

2. What are some foods you eat that you may want to try to
    limit or avoid?

    _____

    _____

    _____

    _____

3. What new foods might you try?

    _____

    _____

    _____

    _____

    _____

    _____

4. Pick one or two foods from the list below and find a recipe online that uses them. Make the recipe or come up with your own idea for a snack or meal. Have a grownup help you make it and share it with your family or friends.

Eat These	Limit or Avoid These
Bananas	Hot dogs
Apples	Hamburgers
Blueberries	Chips
Raspberries	Cheese
Strawberries	Yogurt
Grapes	Ice Cream
Avocados	Eggs
Spinach	Processed lunch meat
Celery	White bread
Cucumbers	White sugar
Arugula	French fries
Broccoli	Anything fried
Sweet potatoes	Pizza
Nuts	Donuts
Coconut	Pancakes
Seeds	Cookies
Wild Rice	Candy
Seaweeds	

15

Water Is
Medicine

1. What are your water drinking habits?

    _____

    _____

    _____

    _____

    _____

    _____

2. What is one goal you could set to improve your river?

    _____

    _____

    _____

    _____

    _____

    _____

    _____

    _____

    _____

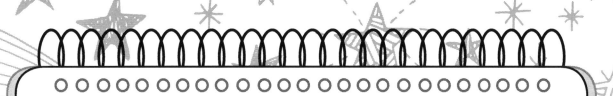

16

Nature Is Medicine

1. What are three activities you like doing outside? Why do you like them?

   _____
   _____
   _____

2. Where do you enjoy walking or hiking? Why? _____

   _____
   _____

3. What inside activity can you give up to get outside more each day?

   _____
   _____
   _____

4. Plan a nature walk with your family. Bring a backpack with water, a healthy snack and a notebook in case you want to record anything. Get out there and do it!

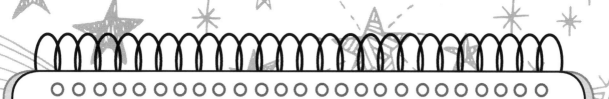

Sleep Is Medicine

1. What is your current bedtime routine like now?_____

    _____

    _____

    _____

    _____

2. What might you change to make it even better?_____

    _____

    _____

    _____

    _____

3. Using the guidelines mentioned in the book, *The Magic of Me*, what time should you be going to bed in order to get the proper amount of sleep for your age?

    _____

    _____

    _____

    _____

18

Forgiveness
Is Medicine

1. Describe a time you felt hurt by another person.

   _____

   _____

   _____

   _____

   _____

   _____

2. Did you forgive him or her? If not, can you forgive him or
   her now?

   _____

   _____

   _____

   _____

   _____

   _____

   _____

   _____

19

Dangerous Addictions

1. Have you felt out of balance because you were too involved with something?

   _____

   _____

   _____

   _____

   _____

   _____

   _____

   _____

2. What could you do instead that would be a better choice?

   _____

   _____

   _____

   _____

   _____

   _____

   _____

   _____

   _____

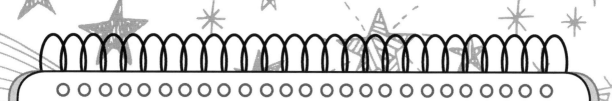

20

Welcome To
Classroom Earth

1. What was a rough time you experienced recently? _____

   _____

   _____

   _____

   _____

   _____

2. Did you learn a lesson from that experience?

   _____

   _____

   _____

   _____

   _____

3. How can you use that lesson in the future?

   _____

   _____

   _____

   _____

   _____

   _____

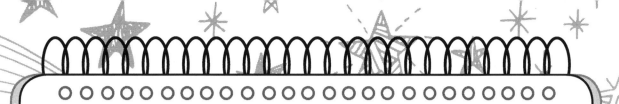

Everyone
Is A Teacher

1. Name any person in your life. What is one lesson that person taught you?

_____

_____

_____

_____

_____

_____

_____

2. Think about a main character in a recent book you've read or movie you watched. What lesson can you learn from that person?

_____

_____

_____

_____

_____

_____

_____

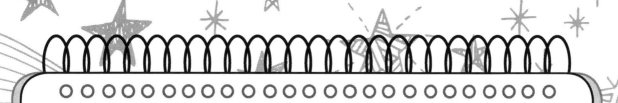

Giving From
The Heart

1. What is one thing or service you could give to a family member?_____

_____

_____

_____

_____

_____

_____

_____

2. What is one thing you could say to a family member or friend that would be a gift?

_____

_____

_____

_____

_____

_____

_____

_____

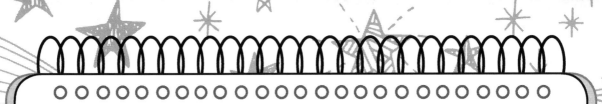

3. Create a banking system for yourself. Use three separate jars or envelopes. Label one *Giving*, one *Savings*, and one *Spending*.

When you get money, talk with your parents how to best divide it up into your different categories.

Enjoy sharing your *giving* money with someone or something you feel passionately about.

Enjoy the *spending* money to purchase things you want.

Money in the *saving* category can be collected for something major you want in your future. Maybe it could be used to pay for college or to buy a car. Let it sit there and pile up or ask your parents to put it in an account that earns interest, or bonus money. See if you can avoid touching it until it's time to make your big purchase.

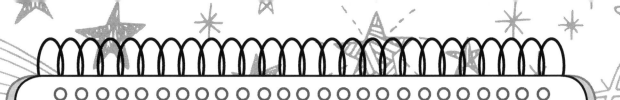

23

Seeking Wisdom

1. What is something you'd like to learn more about? _____

_____

_____

_____

_____

2. What are some ways you could learn about it?

_____

_____

_____

_____

_____

3. Describe something many people may consider normal, but that you don't agree with.

_____

_____

_____

_____

_____

_____

_____

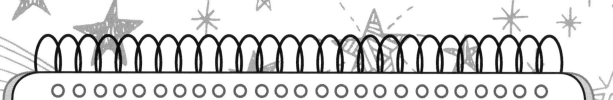

24

The Bully Brain

1. Have you been bullied before? If not, have you seen someone else get bullied? Tell about what happened. _____

   _____
   _____
   _____
   _____

2. Did you think about why the kid acted like a bully? Have
   your thoughts changed at all? If so, explain._____

   _____
   _____
   _____
   _____

3. Is there a time when your words or actions could have
   made someone feel bullied? If so, think about how you
   made the other person feel. _____

   _____
   _____
   _____
   _____
   _____
   _____

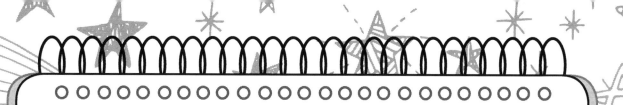

25

Choosing Friends

1. Who is one of your good friends? Why do you like him or her? _____
   _____
   _____
   _____
   _____

2. What qualities make you a good friend?
   _____
   _____
   _____
   _____
   _____

3. What qualities do you want in a friend?
   _____
   _____
   _____
   _____
   _____

26

Saying
See You Later

1. Do you have any loved ones in spirit?

_____

_____

_____

_____

_____

_____

_____

2. Have you ever felt they are with you or have you received
   a sign from them?

_____

_____

_____

_____

_____

_____

_____

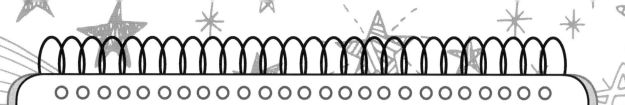

27

What Is God?

1. How would you explain God to someone?

_____

_____

_____

_____

_____

_____

_____

_____

2. Tell about something you might ask for in your prayers.

_____

_____

_____

_____

_____

_____

_____

_____

_____

_____

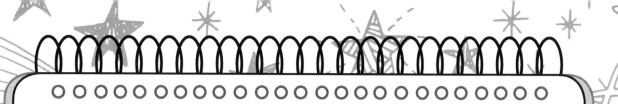

28

Are Angels Real?

1. Have you ever felt an angel in your life?

_____

_____

_____

_____

_____

_____

_____

2. Have you ever called upon God's angels to help you? Can you think of a time when you could have asked for help?

_____

_____

_____

_____

_____

_____

_____

_____

29

What Are Spirit Guides?

1. How does it make you feel to know that you have an entire team in spirit guiding you?

_____
_____
_____
_____
_____
_____
_____

2. What might you ask for guidance on?

_____
_____
_____
_____
_____
_____
_____
_____

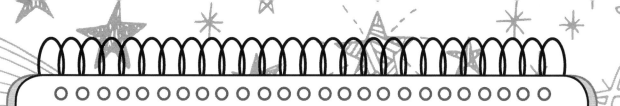

30

Why Are We Here?

1. Name a famous person you know a lot about. What do you think they may have come to Earth to do or learn?

   _____

   _____

   _____

   _____

   _____

   _____

   _____

2. Interview a few grandparents or older adults. Ask them to tell you about some of the most important lessons they have learned in life.

   _____

   _____

   _____

   _____

   _____

   _____

   _____

   _____

Gratitude Journal

Today I am grateful for . . .

_____

_____

_____

_____

_____

_____

_____

_____

_____

_____

_____

_____

_____

_____

_____

_____

_____

_____

_____

_____

_____

_____

_____

Gratitude Journal

Today I am grateful for . . .
_____
_____
_____
_____
_____
_____
_____
_____
_____
_____
_____
_____
_____
_____
_____
_____
_____
_____
_____
_____
_____
_____

Gratitude Journal

Today I am grateful for . . .
_____
_____
_____
_____
_____
_____
_____
_____
_____
_____
_____
_____
_____
_____
_____
_____
_____
_____
_____
_____
_____
_____
_____

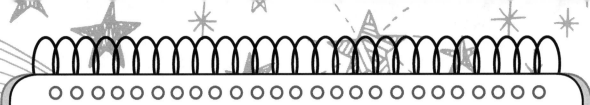

Gratitude Journal

Today I am grateful for . . .

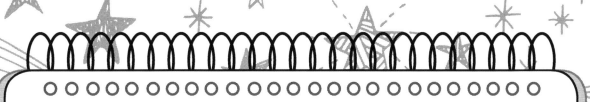

Gratitude Journal

Today I am grateful for . . .

_____

_____

_____

_____

_____

_____

_____

_____

_____

_____

_____

_____

_____

_____

_____

_____

_____

_____

_____

_____

_____

_____

Gratitude Journal

Today I am grateful for . . .

_____

_____

_____

_____

_____

_____

_____

_____

_____

_____

_____

_____

_____

_____

_____

_____

_____

_____

_____

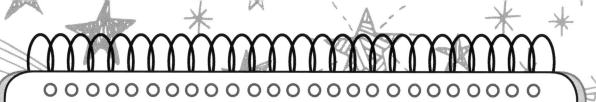

Gratitude Journal

Today I am grateful for . . .
_____

_____
_____
_____
_____
_____
_____
_____
_____
_____
_____
_____
_____
_____
_____
_____
_____
_____
_____
_____
_____
_____
_____
_____

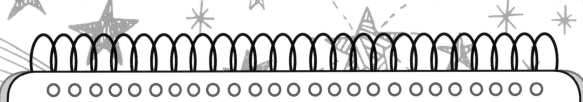

Gratitude Journal

Today I am grateful for . . .
_____
_____
_____
_____
_____
_____
_____
_____
_____
_____
_____
_____
_____
_____
_____
_____
_____
_____
_____
_____
_____
_____

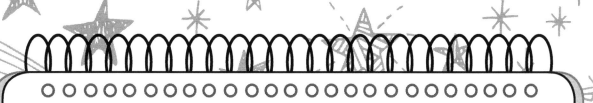

Gratitude Journal

Today I am grateful for . . .

_____

_____
_____
_____
_____
_____
_____
_____
_____
_____
_____
_____
_____
_____
_____
_____
_____
_____
_____
_____
_____
_____
_____
_____

Gratitude Journal

Today I am grateful for . . .

_____
_____
_____
_____
_____
_____
_____
_____
_____
_____
_____
_____
_____
_____
_____
_____
_____
_____
_____
_____
_____
_____

Gratitude Journal

Today I am grateful for . . .

_____

_____

_____

_____

_____

_____

_____

_____

_____

_____

_____

_____

_____

_____

_____

_____

_____

_____

_____

_____

_____

_____

_____

_____

Made in the USA
San Bernardino, CA
09 January 2020